OPPOSITES

Hello...

NICK BUTTERWORTH
AND
MICK INKPEN

Hodder
Children's
Books

A division of Hodder Headline plc

Black and white

Fast and slow

Up...

and down

Big and little

Quiet and loud

First...

and last

Nice and nasty

Fat and thin

Hot…

and cold

Hard and soft

Long and short

On...

and off

Rough and smooth

Weak and strong

Day...

and night

Wet and dry

Old and new

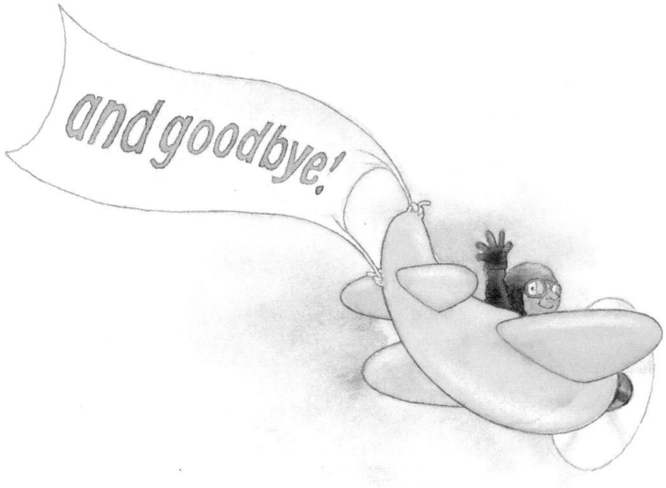
and goodbye!